Amish Health Secrets

**Proven Home Remedies, Recipes,
Cleaning and Gardening Tips**

By: Tony Parker

IMPORTANT NOTICE

This book is intended as a record of folklore and historical solutions and is composed of tips, suggestions, and remembrances. It is sold with the understanding that the publisher is not engaged in rendering medical advice and does not intend this as a substitute for medical care by qualified professionals. No claims are intended as to the safety, or endorsing the effectiveness, of any of the remedies which have been included and the publisher cannot guarantee the accuracy or usefulness of individual remedies in this collection.

The information in this book is meant to be used in conjunction with the guidance of your health care professional. The remedies described here are neither advice nor prescriptions, but provided for educational purposes only. If you think you have a medical problem then please seek qualified professional help immediately. In the event that you use this information without your doctor's approval, you ar prescribing for yourself which is your constitutional right, but the publisher and author assume no responsibility. If you cannot accept these conditions, then you may return this book in new condition for a refund.

If you have a medical problem you should consult a physician.

Printing 12 11 10 9 8 7 6 5 4 3 2

ISBN: 978-1-62397-031-4

First Edition

Published by
James Direct, Inc.
500 S. Prospect Ave.
Hartville, OH 44632

TABLE OF CONTENTS

INTRODUCTION

The Amish in America are descendants of a group of early 1550's European Christians called "Anabaptists." Many escaped religious persecution fleeing to Switzerland, where they became known as Mennonites, named after the Dutch Anabaptist leader, Menno Simons. In 1693 a group of Mennonites led by Jakob Amman broke away and became known as the Amish.

The first group of Amish arrived in America around 1730 near Lancaster County. Pennsylvania. The Amish have settled in about two dozen states, Canada and South America, though about 80 percent are located in Pennsylvania, Ohio and Indiana. Today, the Amish continue to subscribe to Christian beliefs, combining their faith in their entire culture. They place all emphasis on the community rather than the individual, and live separately from the outside world, without modern technology and conveniences.

To the average 21st century individual, the physical work and inconvenience of the Amish lifestyle may seem backward. They grow their own food using 19th century farming techniques requiring hard physical labor. They make their own clothing, build their own communities, all without the benefit of electricity. In fact, according to a survey published in the journal *Medicine & Science in Sports and Exercise,* the Amish participate in roughly six times the amount of weekly physical activity performed in modernized nations.

What is the payoff? Only about four percent of the Amish surveyed were obese and about 26 percent were overweight. In contrast, about 31 percent of American adults are obese and about 65 percent are overweight. The researchers concluded that a physically active lifestyle played a critical role in keeping our ancestors fit and healthy.

Doctors have discovered that the Amish have lower rates of cancer and heart disease than the average American. According to the *U.S. Center for Disease Control* they also have lower incidences of high blood pressure and *University of Tennessee* research shows they have lower rates of obesity. In addition, the *American Society for Bone and Mineral Research* found that they have higher bone density and 42% fewer hip fractures. Their active lifestyle certainly plays a part in their overall good health. But they also are very proactive and take good care of themselves.

The Amish believe that good mental and physical health is a gift from God, but it is their responsibility to take care of it. They believe that prayer plays and important part in healing, along with folk remedy practices including faith healing and herbal treatments. In a recent study by the *University of Iowa,* 95 percent of Amish people surveyed report using folk remedies - a practice consistent with their need to be self sufficient.

In an emergency, an Amish person will seek modern medical treatment, but their folk remedies continue to play and important role in the culture and health of the Amish.

The ultimate goal of the Amish is to live by God's teachings... and their lifestyle reflects this. They have a saying: *"You can preach a better sermon with your life than your lips."* The Amish try to set a good example with the way they live and use proverbs and sayings to teach and inspire.

This volume of home remedies, tips and recipes was collected from Amish families in Ohio, Indiana, Pennsylvania and elsewhere.

HEALTH REMEDIES

*I've found a little remedy
to ease the life we live
that costs the least and does the most
it is the word "Forgive."*

This volume of home remedies, tips and recipes was collected from Amish families in Ohio, Indiana, Pennsylvania and elsewhere. Unfortunately, some submitted remedies did not include complete usage instructions.

Allergies

Honey is anti-bacterial. It can help seasonal hay fever or pollen allergies. It is best to use local honey, if possible. One tsp. a day by mouth until allergy season is over.

Artery Health

- Mix 1 cup Lecithin and 1 cup Wheat Germ. Take 2 Tbsp. a day.
- Take 1 tsp. Omega 3 Fish Oil a day.

Arthritis

10 tsp. Apple Cider Vinegar to a glass of Water at each meal. Use Honey instead of Sugar.

Arthritis Helper

6   Lemons
6   Grapefruits

6 Oranges
4 Tbsp. Epsom Salts
4 cups boiling Water

Grind whole fruits; mix together. Sprinkle Epsom Salts on top. Pour boiling water over it; let set overnight. Put into a cloth bag and squeeze out all the juice. Take 3 Tbsp. 3 times a day. Improvement should be noticed in 6 weeks.

Asthma

- For Asthma never use Fabric Softener in laundry. Use Vinegar for rinse.
- Placing a cold wet rag on your forehead can help relieve a suffocating feeling.

Athlete's Foot

Soak feet in a solution of 3/4 cup apple cider vinegar and lightly sprinkle baking soda in shoes and socks.

Bedsores

Make a patty of Sugar and Peroxide. Put a cloth or towel over it and fasten it somehow. Bread soaked in milk and applied is good for infection.

Bee Stings

- Mix equal parts Baking Soda & Vinegar and put on Bee Stings.
- Place a slice of Onion or vinegar on sting.
- Mix equal parts Baking Soda and Vinegar and put on Bee Stings.

Blood Cleanse

2 tsp. Wheat Germ
2 tsp. Lecithin
- Mix the above ingredients in an 8 oz. glass of Water.
- Drink 6 to 8 ounces of Beet Juice a day.

Body Odor

As an experiment, took very high doses of Dandelion Root (2 heaping teaspoonfuls per day), an unexpected side effect was that body odor was reduced so much that I used Deodorant more out of habit than needed. Dandelion is safe for long term use, if you do try it, start with a low dose.

Boils

Place a poultice of equal parts linseed oil, flour and honey on boil.

Bowel Troubles

To have bowels move every day, eat raw Bran, 5 rounded tablespoons daily. I eat it all for breakfast with fruit juice and honey and cream.

Bronchitis Cough

Steep a few Mullein Leaves in hot Water. Strain and sweeten with Honey. Drink before going to bed.

Burns

- Aloe Vera is called the burn plant, because it inhibits the action of a pain producing peptide and it helps healing and skin growth. If you buy Aloe in the form of a cream or processed gel, make sure it contains at least 70 percent Aloe. Or just keep an Aloe Plant nearby. Simply break off a leaf, split it open and rub the soothing juice over the burn.
- If you burn your tongue from hot food or drinks, put sugar on your tongue.
- Put Apple Cider Vinegar on the burned area immediately. This will prevent any blistering.

Calluses, Corns and Spurs

Heat enough Caster Oil in a pan to soak your feet for 15 minutes. Twice a day. This will help Spurs.

Canker Sores

Daub the affected area with Apple Cider Vinegar.

Car Sickness

- Ginger Powder to prevent Car Sickness. Try giving 1/2 tsp. Ginger Powder, ten minutes before leaving home. We found it very effective for our family. Also good to prevent headaches. Take 1/2 tsp. before going away. This will soothe the stomach.
- For car sickness, take Ginger Pills before and during travel, as needed.

Carpal Tunnel

Place the palm of one hand against the 4 fingers of the other hand and bend the fingers back till it hurts. Hold for 30 seconds. Repeat as often as needed.

Chapped Hands

Put 1/2 tsp. Salt in the palm of your hands. Pour 1 tsp. Vegetable Oil over salt. Rub your hands together for about 5 minutes. Rinse with warm water. Pat dry. Salt heals & your skin will be soft.

Chest Rub

Rub Castor Oil on chest and back. Cover with a warm cloth. This will not blister, so you can put the linament on heavily. In severe cases, repeat every 2 or 3 hours. This almost never fails for Bronchitis, chest tightness and Pneumonia.

Cold Plaster

1 tsp. each of Cinnamon, Cloves, Nutmeg and Allspice. Plus 1/2 tsp. each of Ginger and Mustard. Mix with enough Lard to make a salve. Put onto cloth and apply to chest or throat.

Colds, Coughs and Flu Prevention

Take 1 tsp. Raw Garlic chopped fine with 1 tsp. of Apple Cider Vinegar in a 1/2 cup of warm Water. Take it in evenings before you go to bed. This keep the Flu, Colds away!

Colds and Coughs

- Fry Onions in fat, strain and use ointment for Chest rub.
- Seeds of Fenugreek, put in a 1/2 cup boiling Water, let it set for 15 minutes. Sweeten with honey. Fenugreek breaks up phlegm and Mucus. Then use Slippery Elm Tea to help remove them from the body.
- Bathe in Dry Mustard & Vinegar water if you have a cold or the flu.
- Soak feet in hot Water, put in Vinegar, Red Pepper, Mustard.
- For colds and coughs try rubbing Swedish Bitters over the nose. Do it often. It really works. For coughs, put an Onion Poultice on the chest overnight. It really helps to loosen a tight cough.
- After going to bed, rub the feet soles with Vicks® salve.

Colds or Sinus

Mix 1   cup Real Lemon®
  1/2   cup Honey
  1/2   cup Vinegar
         Take 1/4 cup of the syrup at bedtime as needed.

Colon Health

- Take 1 teaspoon of psyllium powder in 8 ounces of water two hours before bed.
- Drink flaxseed or peppermint tea in the evening.

Constipation

  1   pint hot Water
  2   Tbsp. Epsom Salts
1/2   Tbsp. Cream of Tarter
       Drink first thing in morning about 1 cup full or more if needed. To be used occasionally when the need arises.
- Use equal amounts of All Bran® Cereal, Applesauce and Prune Juice. Take 3 or 4 Tbsp. a day.

Cracked Fingers

Try washing them with cold water. Soap and hot water washes the oil out of the skin. For itchy skin, try washing with Borax®.

Cradle Cap

Try rubbing Olive Oil on scalp every evening before going to bed. In the morning shampoo it out.

Cramps

- Apply a poultice of catnip to the abdomen for menstrual cramps.
- For general cramps hot ginger tea may help.

Dandruff

- Add some Tea Tree Oil to your rinsing water when washing your hair.
- Put a few drop of Tea Tree Oil into your shampoo to get rid of dandruff.

Dehydration

1 qt. Water
8 level tsp. White Sugar
1/2 tsp.

Salt Stir the above ingredients together until all powder is dissolved. Sip a little every 5 minutes.

Diarrhea

- Mix 1 Tbsp. Cornstarch in Milk or Fruit Juice & drink it.
- Drink 1/2 cup warm Water with Family Tincture. Also hot Milk with Salt and Pepper is good for stomach.

Diabetes

With your doctor's approval increase fiber intake... eat beans, oatmeal and artichokes.

Digestion

Use olive oil, prune juice, and yogurt. Also take a probiotic.

Ear Ache

- Rub pure Peppermint Oil over and around ear.
- For an earache, put warm Onion slices on your ears.
- Slice a raw Potato, wrap it in a Paper Towel. Warm it a little, put on both ears. You have to put on a scarf or something to hold it in place.

Energy Boost

When your energy is low, eat a teaspoon of raw, unfiltered honey. It goes directly to your brain and gives you a boost.

Eye Health

Take bilberry supplements.

Fainting

A drink of Vinegar is a sure cure for fainting.

Fever

- Put fried onions in an old stocking and put on feet overnight. It also helps to

soak feet in a bucket of warm to hot water with 1 cup Vinegar added.
- Wrap a towel out around your head that has been wet with Vinegar. Then wrap a dry one around over it.
- If you have a fever, put Onions on your feet or wash off with Vinegar Water.
- If you are sick, or have a fever, take about a gallon or so of warm Water (as hot as you can stand it). Cut up a small Onion & some Dry Mustard and put it in the Water, put your feet in there for half an hour or so. That also feels good if you have a long and tired day.

Flu
- Put some Vinegar & Dry Mustard in your bath water and soak for awhile.
- For flu, take one tsp. Elderberry daily.

Frostbite
Apply one ounce each of olive oil, ammonia and peppermint oil to area. Seek medical care.

Gallstones
Drink 1/2 gallon Apple Juice each day for 3 days. On the 3rd night after 3 days of drinking Juice, mix 2 ounces Lemon Juice with 2 ounces of Olive Oil and drink. Lay on your right side for 1/2 hour before going to bed. The stones will pass without pain and be in your first bowel movement the next day and look like small peas.

Gas
Drink ginger tea.

Gout
Cut down on the amount of meat you eat and eat fresh cherries or drink cherry juice.

Grape Juice Diet:
Drink 24 oz. Grape Juice in morning, sipping it slowly, and have it done by 10:00AM. Eat normally the rest of the day, but avoid pork for best results. It is recommended to use the Grape Juice unsweetened and for at least 2 weeks at a time. This is good for many ailments.

Fight Gingivitis Infection

Mix Salt, Baking Soda and brush teeth. Can also gargle with a solution of Salt and Water.

Hair Care

Massage well beaten egg whites to scalp. Let stand for 2 minutes. Rinse.

Hair Loss

- Take Bio B-100®, Vitamin A, B Complex for hair loss. Ask for it at a health food store. Also, make 1 pint Strong Sage Tea and add 1 Tbsp. Boric Acid. Massage the scalp daily with this solution.
- Rub Aloe Vera juice into scalp.

Headache

- Massage a drop of Lavender Oil between your thumb and forefinger (The Acupuncture Point).
- For headaches, rub Eucalyptus & Peppermint Oil on forehead.

Heartburn

- Mix 6 ounces water with 1/2 tsp. Baking Soda.
- To ease Heartburn, drink 12 ounces plain Whole Milk.

Heart Health

Drink a tea of hawthorn berries.

Hemorrhoids

Mixing Psyllium Powder and Water can help ease the pain of hemorrhoids.

Hiccups

- To get relief from hiccups, eat one tsp. Peanut Butter, if you are not allergic to peanuts.
- Put 1/2 tsp. cream of tarter in 1 cup water. Take 2 tbsp. on empty stomach.

High Blood Pressure

Eat Apples, Grapes, Cranberries or their juice. Bananas, Broccoli, Celery and Cayenne Pepper are also good for you.

Infections
Honey is a natural Penicillin. Put right on minor cuts.

Insect Bites
The best remedy for any kind of bite or sting is to find some Plantain, crush the leaves or chew them a little and put on the bite.

Insomnia
Drink Hops tea or Valerian tea before bed.

Joint Pain
For painful joints, try M.S.M. Very helpful for knees. It can be obtained at health food stores.

Kidney Trouble:
Take Zinc, Magnesium and vitamin B-6. Cherry Juice, Ground Cranberries and Corn Silk Tea all help. Also Asparagus cooked in lots of water. Drink some every day. Eat less red meat and drink less Coffee.

Kidney, Bladder Trouble
For Kidney and Bladder trouble, to pass off excess fluid, try Peach Tree Leaves and make a tea. Drink one to two cups daily. One cup in evening before going to bed is very good.

Leg Cramps
To keep those leg cramps away, take Vitamin E before going to bed.

Lemonade Cleansing Diet
2   Tbsp. Lemon Juice
2   Tbsp. Maple Syrup
1/10   tsp. Red Pepper

Or take Red Pepper in Capsules. Combine the Juice & Maple Syrup in a 10 oz. glass & fill with hot water. Cold water may be used if desired, 6-12 glasses a day. 2 tsp. Sea Salt to a quart of lukewarm water.

First day after diet: Several 8 oz. glasses of fresh Orange Juice as desired during the day. Drink it slowly.

Second day: Drink several glasses of Orange Juice during the day with extra water if needed. In the P.M., prepare Vegetable Soup by boiling together

Potatoes, Carrots & Celery. Have this soup for the evening meal using the broth mostly.

Third day: Drink Orange Juice in the morning and at noon. Have some more soup in the evening. Eat whatever is desired in the form of Vegetables, Salads or Fruits. No Meat or Eggs, Bread or Pastries.

Lint Remover

Add a yard of Nylon Netting to your dryer with the wet Clothes. It will catch most of the Lint.

Liver Health

- Take milk thistle supplement.
- Drink beet juice.

Memory

Garlic can keep your mental edge sharp. Eat 1-3 cloves of Garlic each day dipped in honey or chocolate.

Menopause

Drink a tea of rosemary, Shepherd's Purse, Elder and Peppermint. Drink 2 cups a day as needed.

Menstrual

Chew fennel seeds thoroughly for discomfort.

Nervousness

Valerian tea and Hops is said to help calm nerves.

Mosquito Bite Relief

Moisten a bar of soap and rub on the bite. It will stop itching and act as disinfectant to prevent infection.

Mouth Sores, Cold Sores

Mix 1 tsp. each of cayenne pepper and goldenseal in 1 quart water. Rinse mouth. Do not swallow.

Muscle Aches

- Try rubbing Olive Oil into the sore areas before going to bed
- For **backache, foot pain** and **knee pain.** Make an ointment of 1 Tbsp. cayenne powder to 1 pint apple cider vinegar. Boil about 10 minutes. Allow to cool and apply slightly warm.

Nasal Drops

3/4   tsp. Salt
  4   oz. Water

Combine the Salt and Water. Put 1 drop in each nostril as often as needed. Dr. recommended!

Nervous Stomach

Try Aloe Vera Juice. It is the best thing I have ever taken for nerves, and I too have a nervous stomach.

Nose Bleed

Drinking 2 Tbsp. full of Vinegar in about 4 oz. of water has stopped nose bleeding when all other methods failed.

Oily Skin

Witch Hazel is an excellent oil remover. Use a clean cotton ball to dab some Witch Hazel on your skin to help keep it oil free. I sometimes use Witch Hazel with Aloe Vera formula.

Poison Ivy

Try rubbing the inside of a Banana peel over the affected area. It relieves itching.

Prostate

- Chew pumpkin seeds.
- Eat more vegetables because they contain plant sterols.
- Drink tea from burdock (gletta).
- Drink strong peppermint tea every hour.
- Tea from Pau d'Arco helps.

Puffy Eye Solution

Make a potato patty compress by grating raw potato and wrapping in clean cheesecloth or gauze. Place over your eyes for 20 minutes, while resting. A simpler method is to thinly slice a raw potato and apply the potato directly to the skin. Follow with your favorite eye cream, taking care not to stretch the delicate skin around your eyes.

Restless Legs or Cramps

Put 3 or 4 unwrapped soap pieces between the bottom sheet and mattress. Is said to really work.

Rheumatism

Cut up 6 lemons, 6 grapefruits and six oranges, including peel. Boil in 2 quarts of water 10 minutes then strain and refrigerate. Take 1 Tbsp. 3 times a day.

Ringworm

Wash affected area with tar soap and borax. Add 1/2 tsp. of goldenseal, 1 tsp. bloodroot in 1 pint water. Boil. Allow to cool and apply lotion to area.

Sexual Desire

Chew on ginseng root or take ginseng supplements.

Shingles

Make a solution of mulberry leaves and pine bark. Apply lotion with a warm cloth.

Sinus/Allergies

Try a Tea made of Plantain, or what used to be called "Sy Ore Blatta" (Pig Ears Leaves). Good results.

Sinus Headache

For Sinus Headaches, take a lemon, put through blender, peelings also and eat a teaspoonful every morning you get up. Try it for 2 or 3 months.

Skin Care

For hands, mix 1/4 Olive Oil and 1 tsp. Sugar. Rub ointment on hands.

Can also be used on elbows, knees and feet.

Sore Throat
- Take Vinegar and make it strong with Salt and Cayenne Pepper (black pepper may be used) and gargle often.
- If you have a sore throat, drink Tomato Juice, may add some Sugar for a better taste.
- Gargle with warm Salt Water.
- The scratchiness of a sore throat can be eased with a gargle of 1 tsp. of Vinegar in 1 cup warm Water.

Splinter Removal
- For external use, mix a poultice by combining 3 Tbsp of flaxseed with 3 Tbsp of charcoal in 3/4 cup of hot water. Place thickened mixture on gauze strip and apply to area 3 -6 hours or overnight.
- To remove Splinter, put very hot water in a large mouth bottle and put the affected part over the opening, pressing down hard. The suction and steam will soon remove the Splinter.

Spring Tonic
Cream of Tartar and Epsom Salts in a jar of Water. Take 2-3 swallows each morning.

Stop Bleeding:
Put Cayenne Pepper on a fresh minor wound or cut. Keep putting it on, and it will stop. Do not use it to dress an older wound or cut, or it will burn, but it will not burn on a fresh cut or wound.

Sweaty Feet
To prevent the unpleasantness of perspiring feet, place Oatmeal or Bran in the socks.

Test your Thyroid
A simple Thyroid test you can do yourself. After you've slept for at least 4 hours at night, take your temperature. It should read between 97.7 and 98.2. Anything lower indicates Under Active Thyroid and higher indicates Over Active Thyroid. Do not get out of bed before taking temperature. Have thermometer

ready on nightstand within easy reach.

Think Clearer

To enable yourself to think more clearly, eat 3 pecan halves daily.

Tired?

- Mix 1 Tbsp. Cider Vinegar and 1 Tbsp. Honey in a glass of water. Take syrup upon rising in the morning and before every meal. This is good for aches & pains and many other things.
- Take one Tbsp. Pure Cider Vinegar and one Tbsp. Honey in a glass of water. Take before every meal or especially upon rising every morning.

Toothache

- Hold Salt in your hand, the side it hurts, till it relieves.
- To relieve a toothache, wet a small piece of cotton with Vanilla and put it on the aching tooth. To rid yourself of a nasty toothache, put some Epsom Salts directly on the sore tooth.

Toothpaste

- Brush teeth with Baking Soda and Salt. Even helps clean false teeth.
- Mix Baking Soda and Salt in water for a denture soak.

Tooth Whitener

For White Teeth use: 1 Tbsp. Baking Soda, 1 drop Peppermint Oil and 1 Tbsp. Salt.

Urinary Infections

Baking Soda in bath water may bring some relief from burning sensations that may accompany urinary infections.

Upset Stomach and Diarrhea Relief

1   quart Water (luke warm)
1/4   tsp. Salt
1   Tbsp. Sugar

Mix all ingredients together. Do not take more than one cup at a time. It really helps.

- Cook 1 Tbsp. Rice in 2 cups Water for 20 minutes. Strain, and add enough

Water to make a pint. Sip slowly until all gone. Good Luck!

- For Upset Stomach use: 1 cup Frozen Orange Juice Concentrate, 8 tsp. Real Lemon®, 4 tsp. Karo®, crushed ice to make one pint. Give 2 tsp. every 15 minutes as needed.

Varicose Veins

You can help Varicose Veins in one month. Pat some full strength Vinegar onto the offending veins twice a day. Each morning and evening, drink a glass of water with 2 tsp. of Vinegar in it.

Wart Remover

In the morning, crush a Vitamin A capsule, mix it with just enough Water to make a paste, and apply it directly on the Wart. In the afternoon, apply a drop of Castor Oil; in the evening, apply a drop of Lemon Juice. This should help dissolve the wart.

Weight Loss

- To help lose extra pounds, take 2 tsp. of Real Lemon® Juice after every meal.

Whooping Cough

Take 3 or 4 Chestnut Leaves to 1 pint boiling Water. Steep to a tea and sweeten, Honey is good. Drink 5 or 6 times a day.

Minor Wounds and sores

When there is persistent bleeding, wash the wound off with Pure Cider Vinegar. The vinegar causes the blood to coagulate.

Worms

Use Pumpkin Seed Tea to get rid of worms. Pour a small amount of boiling water over 8 seeds, let set awhile. May be put in juice and sipped during the day. Do this for 3 days, then skip 3 days. Repeat.

HOUSEHOLD TIPS

A grudge is a heavy burden to carry.

Brass and Copper Cleaner
Mix 1 Tbsp. each of Salt and Flour and 2 Tbsp. of 3% Hydrogen Peroxide. Rub on item to be cleaned. Then wash in warm water with Dishwashing Liquid. Rinse and dry with a soft cloth.

Brush and Comb Cleaner
A solution of Baking Soda and hot Water cleans your hair brushes and combs.

Clean Tar Off Clothes
Lestoil® will take the Road Tar out of your dirty clothes.

Cookware Shine Up
You can also use Baby Oil on a soft cloth to shine up a kettle, saucepan handles, knobs and even your buggy and nylon harnesses.

Drain Cleaner & Opener
1   cup Salt
1   cup Baking Soda
1   cup Apple Cider Vinegar
Pour each in drain in order given. Rinse with lots of very hot water. Let faucet run for 15 minutes.

Fruit and Vegetable Sanitizing

Soak Add 1/2 tsp. 3% Hydrogen Peroxide to one gallon of water. Soak fruits or vegetables for 15 minutes. Drain. Then soak in clean water 15 minutes. This can help kill bacteria on fruits and vegetables.

Homemade Soap

10	lbs. Grease
1 1/2	lbs. Lye
1	cup Ammonia
4	Tbsp. Borox
1/2	Gal. Rain Water
1/4	cup Gasoline
10	cents worth Sassafras Oil

Put together slowly, once both Grease and Lye mixture are cooled off!

Floor Cleaning

To put on floors for a finish: Use equal amounts of boiled Linseed Oil, Turpentine and Kerosene and a hunk of paraffin, melted. Put on floors hot. Does not get sticky. Wipe off with rags if doesn't all soak in. Put a few coats on new floors.

Ink Removal

To get ink off clothing, use regular hair spray. Spray on, let soak and wipe off. Do this till it's gone.

Oven Cleaner

Make a paste combining 3% Hydrogen Peroxide and Baking Soda. Apply and let stand 15 minutes. Then sponge off using warm water.

Paint Odor

If you paint on the inside, cut Onions in half and lay around to take away the odors.

Pet Cleaner and Deodorizer

Mix 1/4 cup Baking Soda with Ivory® Soap. Be careful to keep out of pet's eyes.

Rust or Grape Juice Stains on Clothing

Moisten stained area with White Vinegar. Then cover area with Salt. Rub gently and rinse using Cold Water.

Scouring Powder for Coffee Stained Cups

Combine equal parts of Salt, Detergent and 3% Hydrogen Peroxide. Pour into cup and let stand. Scrub and rinse.

Sink Cleaner

Sprinkle a Lemon wedge with Salt and use it to scrub your Kitchen Sink clean.

Sink and Tub Cleaner

To shine your Stainless Steel on your sink or baths, use Pure Vinegar, then wipe it dry with a Paper Towel or Cloth.

Spot Remover for Carpets, Upholstery, etc.

Mix Salt , Baking Soda and Dish Washing Liquid with cold water. Apply to stain and rinse.

Windex® Recipe

1 pt. Rubbing Alcohol
3 Tbsp. Liquid Detergent
2 Tbsp. Ammonia
3 drops of Blue Food Coloring
Add Water to make 1 gallon.

GARDENING TIPS

*You can bury a lot of troubles
digging in the dirt.*

African Violets

To aid blooming plants, plant a rusty nail in the same pot with your Violets to have many blossoms.

Bird Food

1	cup Lard
1/2	cup Peanut Butter
1/2	cup Sugar
2	cups Water, add Cornmeal & Oatmeal.

Stir till slightly thick then put in feeder. Birds love it.

Cucumbers

What often looks like blight can be worms in the roots, Cucumbers need Lime. Dissolve 1/2 cup Lime in one gallon Water. Add 1 Tbsp. Bleach or Ammonia. Pour on the plants stem and let it soak into the ground.

Flower and Veggie Blight

2 Tbsp. Epsom Salt
1 Tbsp. Baking Soda
1 Tbsp. Brown Sugar
a little Red Pepper

Mix in a sprinkling can of Water (approximately. 2 gallons).

Grape Vines

- Give 1 pt. Epsom Salt to each Grapevine, then cover with Manure, do this when you trim Grapes.
- For problems with grapes falling off and uneven ripening: 1 gallon Wood Ashes, 1 gallon Lime, 1/2 gallon Epsom Salt and 1 handful Sulphur. Mix well and scatter around plant as far as roots would be. Do this in February, March and April, and again in September, October, November. You can also use it on Raspberries, Blackberries. Just a handful to each plant.

Keeps Cut Flowers Fresher Longer

2 qt. Water
1/4 tsp. Bleach
3 Tbsp. Sugar
1/4 tsp. Powdered Alum

Melon and Tomato Bug Insecticide

Mix these ingredients and spray on plants.

1 gallon Water
1 tsp. Baking Powder
1/2 tsp. Household Ammonia
1 tsp. Salt Petre
1 tsp. Epsom Salt

Mosquito Spray

1 cup Joy® detergent
1 gallon Water
1 cup Ammonia
Mix all together.

Pepper Grower

You can get a bumper crop of Peppers with a Epsom Salt spray at blossom time. 1 tsp. per pint of Water.

Planting

Plant beans on the longest day and they won't get bugs.

Prevent Early Blooming

In February or March, put thick layers of Manure around your fruit trees or Rhubarb to prevent early blooming. This keeps the ground frozen longer for your blooming benefits.

Quick-Grow Plant Food

1   Tbsp. Epsom Salt
1   Tbsp. Ammonia
1   tsp. Baking Powder
1   tsp. Salt Petre
1   gallon Rain Water

Mix this and water plants every 2 weeks. Gives them a boost.

Raspberry Plant Food

1   gallon Wood Ashes
1   gallon Lime
Handful of Sulphur

Mix the above items altogether well. Put a handful on each plant once a month in Feb., March and April and again when small berries are on the plant. Use it once again in the Fall.

Good Luck!

Rose Starter

In October cut off healthy Rose slips from many different kinds of bushes. Then stick them several inches into the ground and cover with glass jars. Put along the east side of the house and mulch around the jars too. Make sure they don't get too dry. Earlier I had worked Banana peelings into the soil there, as I knew Roses need lots of Potassium. When all danger of frost is past, uncover the plants and enjoy their first blooms, good luck.

Bigger Strawberry Yields

Put Dutch Soil Concentrate® diluted in Water on Strawberry Plants in August or Sept. Repeat 2 times a month apart.

Transplanting

Mix 1 Tbsp. Epsom Salt
1   Tbsp. Household Ammonia

1 tsp. Salt Petre
1 tsp. Baking Powder in 1 gallon lukewarm Water.
   Add some to every hole as you plant your plants.

Tomato Blight

1 gallon Water
1 Tbsp. Salt Petre
1 Tbsp. Epsom Salt
1 Tbsp. Baking Powder
1 tsp. Ammonia

   Mix well & give one pint to each plant, every two weeks. Don't water them when the sun shines. Also is good for Melons and more. It seems to be a fertilizer for the Tomatoes they hang on better.

Tomato Booster

   To grow the juiciest, biggest, most abundant Tomatoes possible, sprinkle 1 tsp. Epsom Salt into each planting holes. It's the Magnesium in the Epsom Salt that works the magic.

Weed Killer

   Put the hot water from your cold packer while canning, along the sidewalks to kill grass and weeds.

RECIPES

BREAKFASTS AND BREADS

Happiness is something we create in our minds
By Daily Acts of Thoughtfulness
in the Art of Being Kind.

Banana Bread

1/2	cup Shortening
2	Eggs
1/2	tsp. Salt
1	cup Sugar
2	cups Flour
1	tsp. Baking Soda
3	medium Bananas
1/4	cup chopped Nuts

Mash Bananas in medium bowl. Add Sugar, Eggs, Shortening and beat well. Add dry ingredients & mix well. Pour in loaf pan & bake at 350 degrees for 1 hour.

Blueberry Muffins

1	Egg
1/2	cup Milk
1/4	cup Oil
1 1/2	cups Flour
1/2	cup Sugar
2	tsp. Baking Powder
1/2	tsp. Salt
1	cup fresh Blueberries or 3/4 cup can Blueberries

28

Beat the Egg. Add Milk and Oil. Sift together dry ingredients and add. Blend in Blueberries. Fill 12 muffin cups and bake at 400 degrees for 20 to 25 minutes. Good Luck to You!

Breakfast Cereal

10	cups Quick Oatmeal
1 1/2	cups Brown Sugar
1/2	cup Nuts
1/2	cup Coconut
1	tsp. Baking Soda
1	tsp. Salt
2	pkgs. Graham Crackers broken up in small pieces.

Add 1 lb. melted Butter and mix. Toast for 1/2 hour at 200 degrees, can add 1 cup Butterscotch or Chocolate Chips when done toasting.

Dinner Rolls

1 1/2	cup warm Water
2	Tbsp. Yeast
1/2	cup Sugar
2	Eggs
1/2	cup Shortening
1 1/2	tsp. Salt
4 1/2	cups Flour

Dissolve Yeast in warm Water, add Sugar, Salt and Shortening. Stir in Flour and knead until smooth. Cover and let rise until double in size (about 1 hour). Shape into desired roll. Let rise again. Bake at 400 degrees for 10-15 minutes. Brush top with Butter.

Egg Omelet Dish

6	Eggs, beaten
3	slices diced White Bread
1	lb. Bulk Sausage, browned and drained thoroughly
2	cups Milk
1	cup shredded Velveeta® Cheese
1	tsp. Salt
1	tsp. Dry Mustard

Mix and let set until next morning. Pour into a greased 9" x 12" dish and bake at 350 degrees 40 to 50 minutes, until light brown. A Good Breakfast!

Favorite Biscuits

2	cups Flour
1	Tbsp. Baking Powder
1/2	tsp. Salt
1/4	cup Shortening
1	beaten Egg
3/4	cup Milk
1	Tbsp. Butter melted

In medium bowl mix together dry ingredients, cut in Lard. In small bowl combine the Egg & Milk. Add all at once to dry mixture. Bake in 450 degree oven for 10 to 12 minutes or until golden brown.

Flaky Biscuits

2	cups sifted Flour
3	Tbsp. Sugar
1/2	tsp. Cream of Tarter
3/4	cup Milk, room temperature
4	tsp. Baking Powder
1/2	tsp. Salt
1/2	cup Butter, chilled

In large mixing bowl, sift together Flour, Baking Powder, Sugar, Salt and Cream of Tarter. Cut in Butter until bits are size of Peas. Mix in Milk, only until ingredients are blended. Do not over-mix. Form into a ball. Pat out on floured board to 3/4 inch thickness. Cut with a Biscuit Cutter 2 1/2 inches in size. Place on ungreased cookie sheet or pan. Bake 10 minutes at 470 degrees or until golden brown. Makes 10 biscuits.

Granola

12	cups Quick Oats
1/2	box Rice Krispies®
4	cups Brown Sugar
2	cups Olive Oil
4	Tbsp. Butter flavor
3	tsp. Baking Soda
4	cups Whole Wheat Flour

2   cups Coconut
4   tsp. Salt

Mix well. Toast in oven until golden brown, stirring often so it doesn't get lumpy, let coo!, add raisins to suit your taste.

Sausage and Egg Breakfast

6   Eggs
2   cups Milk
2   slices Bread (cubes)
1   tsp. Salt
1   tsp. Mustard
1/2 lb. Sausage, browned
1/2 cup grated Cheese
1   cup Potatoes, cooked & shredded

Drain Sausage, beat Eggs, Milk, Salt and Mustard. Add Bread and mix well. Add Cheese, Sausage and Potatoes. Pour into greased 9" x 12" baking dish. Bake 45 minutes at 350 degrees. Can be made ahead and refrigerated.

Zucchini Bread

3   Eggs
1   cup Oil
1   cup Honey
3   tsp. Vanilla
2   cups grated Zucchini
3   cups Wheat Flour
1   tsp. Baking Soda
3   tsp. Cinnamon
1/4 tsp. Baking Powder
2/3 cup Nuts, chopped

Mix Oil, Honey, Vanilla and Zucchini; mix lightly but well. Add dry ingredients. Mix until blended, then add Nuts. Pour into two greased bread pans. Bake at 325 degrees for one hour. Remove and cool on wire racks! Good Luck!

Zucchini Squares

1/2 cup Vegetable Oil
1/2 cup chopped Onion

1/2   cup Cheese-shredded
2   Tbsp. Parsley
1/2   tsp. Salt
1/2   tsp. Oregano
1/2   tsp. Seasoned Salt
dash of Pepper
4   Eggs, beaten
1   Clove Garlic or Garlic Salt
1   cup Bisquick®
3   cups Zucchini, unpeeled & shredded

Beat Eggs then add, Oil, Onion, Cheese, Parsley & seasonings. Stir in Bisquick® and fold in Zucchini. Spread in a greased cake pan. Bake 25-30 minutes at 350 degrees.

COOKIES, CAKES AND DESSERTS

A pound of Patience you must find
Mixed well with Loving Words so kind
Drop in two pounds of helping deeds
And thoughts of other peoples needs
A pack of Smiles, to make the crust
Then stir and bake it well you must

Amish Cake

1/2	cup Butter
2 2/3	cups Brown Sugar
2	tsp. Baking Soda
2	tsp. Vanilla
2	cups Sour Milk
3	cups Flour
1	Tbsp. distilled White Vinegar
1	cup Milk

Mix and Bake at 350 degrees.

Topping:

1	cup Brown Sugar
1/2	cup Sweet Cream
4	Tbsp. Butter
1	Tbsp. Light Karo®

Bring to a boil, then add 1/2 cup coconut, 1/2 cup chopped Walnuts. Boil 4 minutes longer. Put on top of cake.

Apple Cake

2 cups Sugar
2 cups Flour
1/2 cup Butter
4 cups sliced Apples
1/2 tsp. Cinnamon
2 tsp. Baking Soda
2 Eggs

In bowl mix together Sugar, Eggs & Butter till fluffy. Add dry ingredients & Apples. Bake at 350 degrees for 45 minutes. Very moist & good, needs no icing.

Apple Goodie

3/4 cup White Sugar
1/2 tsp. Cinnamon
1 Tbsp. Flour
1/8 tsp. Salt
2 cups Sliced Apples

Topping:

1/2 cup Oatmeal
1/2 cup Brown Sugar
1/2 cup Flour
1/4 cup Butter
1/8 tsp. Baking Soda
1/8 tsp. Baking Powder

Sift together Sugar, Flour, Salt and Cinnamon. Combine with Sliced Apples. Mix well and place in the bottom of a greased casserole or pan. To make topping, combine dry ingredients and cut in Butter to make crumbs. Put crumbs on top of Apple mixture. Bake at 375 degrees for 35-40 minutes. Serve hot or cold with Milk. Also good with Ice Cream.

Barb's Favorite Coconut Cake

1 1/4 cups Shortening
3 3/4 cups Sugar
4 Eggs
5 1/2 cups Flour
5 tsp. Baking Powder

2   tsp. Salt
2   1/2 cups Milk
3   tsp. Vanilla
2   cups Coconut

Cream Sugar and Shortening; beat in Eggs. Sift together dry ingredients and stir in alternately with Milk and Vanilla. Add Coconut last. Pour into two greased 9" x 13" pans. Bake at 350 degrees for 35-40 minutes.

Brown Betty

2 1/2   cups sliced Apples
1   cup Flour
1/2   tsp. Salt
1/2   tsp. Baking Soda
1/2   cup Brown Sugar
1/2   cup Butter
1   cup Rolled Oats

Put Apples in bottom of greased 9" x 13" cake pan. Mix the rest together and put on top of Apples. Bake at 375 35-40 minutes, then serve warm with milk.

Bushel Cookies

2   Eggs
7/8   cup Lard
1 2/3   cup Sugar
1 1/4   cup Milk
1   tsp. Baking Soda
1   Tbsp. Baking Powder
2   Tbsp. Maple Flavored Karo®
6   oz. Raisins and 3 oz. Salted Peanuts, ground together
1   cup Quick Cooking Oats
1   lb Flour (about 3 cups)

Mix in order given and drop by spoonfuls on cookie sheet. Bake at 375 degrees to 400 degrees till browned. Very good, chewy, Holiday season treat. Makes about 1 1/2 gal. cookies. Enough to share-more to spare!

Butterscotch Pie

     2   cups Brown Sugar
3 1/2   cups Boiling Water
   1/2   tsp. Salt
     1   tsp. Vanilla
   1/2   cup Butter
         * Boil these ingredients and set aside.
     3   Eggs
     1   cup White Sugar
1 1/3   cups Flour
     3   cups Milk
pinch of salt
         * Mix and add to brown sauce and cook until thick. Pour into 3 baked pie shells.

Cake Tip

When creaming Butter & Sugar for a cake, add a little hot water, makes a finer cake and creams easier. Brush cream, then sprinkle sugar on top of two crust pies, browns beautifully.

Can't Leave Alone Bars

     2   Cake Mixes Yellow & White
     4   Eggs
   1/2   stick Butter
     1   can Sweetened Condensed Milk
   2/3   cup Oil
     1   cup Chocolate Chips

Mix cake mixes, oil and eggs together. Spread all but 3/4 cup into a 9" x 13" cake pan. Melt Milk, Chocolate Chips and Butter together. Put on top of cake, then cover with remaining cake mix. Bake at 350 degrees for 20-30 minutes. Don't over bake.

Caramel Custard Pie

Beat 2 Egg Yolks, add 2 cups Brown Sugar, 2 Tbsp. melted Butter, 1/2 tsp. Salt, stir, add 2 Tbsp. Flour and 2 cups Milk. Last add 2 well beaten Egg Whites, stir gently. Can also sprinkle a few Pecans on top. Bake at 325 degrees till done. Don't boil or it'll be watery.

Quick Cheese Cake

Crust:

7   Graham Crackers (crushed)
1   Tbsp. Powder Sugar
Butter (melted)

Press 3/4 of mixture in bottom of pan.

Mix and let cool.

3   oz. Jell-O® (any flavor)
8   oz. Cream Cheese
1   tsp. Vanilla
1   cup boiling Water
1   cup Sugar
2   cups Cream

Mix the Cheese mixture and add cooled Jell-O®. Put remaining crumbs on top.

Chocolate Chip Cookies

1   cup Crisco®
3/4   cup Brown Sugar
3/4   cup White Sugar
2   Eggs
1   pkg. Chocolate Chips
3   cups Flour
1   tsp. Baking Soda
1/2   tsp. Salt
1   tsp. Vanilla
1   cup Chopped Nuts

Bake at 375 degrees until lightly browned..

Chocolate Chip Cookies

1   cup Oil
1/2   cup Sugar
1   cup Brown Sugar
1   tsp. Vanilla
2   Eggs well beaten
2 1/2 cups Whole Wheat Flour
1   tsp. Baking Soda

1   tsp. Salt
1   cup Chocolate Chips
    Bake at 375 degrees.

Cinnamon Candy Popcorn

8   quarts plain Popcorn
a little Salt
1   cup Butter or Oleo
1/2 cup Light Corn Syrup
9   oz. Red Hots® Candies

Place Popcorn in a large bowl and set aside. In a saucepan, combine Oleo, Corn Syrup and Candies. Bring to a boil over medium heat. Stirring constantly. Boil 5 minutes, stirring constantly. Pour over Popcorn, mix thoroughly. Turn into greased pans. Bake at 250 degrees for 1 hour stirring every 15 minutes. Remove from pans, let cool. Break apart and store in airtight containers.

Coconut Oatmeal Pie

3   Eggs, well beaten
1   cup Karo®
1   cup Brown Sugar
2   Tbsp. Butter
1/3 cup Quick Cooking Oats
2/3 cup Coconut
1   tsp. Vanilla
1   unbaked Pie Shell

Blend all ingredients and pour into pie shell. Bake at 350 degrees for 30-35 minutes.

Dairy Queen Ice Cream

2   Tbsp. Gelatin
1/2 cup cold Water
4   cups Milk
1 1/2 cups Sugar
2   tsp. Vanilla
1/3 tsp. Salt
3   cups Cream

Soak Gelatin in cold Water. Heat the Milk to hot, but not boiling. Remove from heat. Add Gelatin, Sugar, Vanilla & Salt. Cool, then add Cream. Put in a cold place to chill for 5-6 hours before freezing. Yield 1 gallon.

Date Pudding

1 cup Dates (chopped fine)
1 cup boiling Water
2 tsp. baking Soda

> Pour hot Water over Dates, let stand until lukewarm, then add Soda.
> Add

1 cup Brown Sugar
1 1/2 cups Flour
1/2 cup Nuts
2 beaten Eggs
2 Tbsp. Shortening

> Combine and add to above ingredients, Bake at 350 for 30 minutes.

Deep Dark Chocolate Cake

2 cups Flour
2 cups Sugar
1/2 cup Cocoa
1 1/2 tsp. Baking Soda
1 1/2 tsp. Baking Powder
1 cup boiling Water
1 tsp. Salt
2 Eggs
1 cup Milk
1/2 cup Vegetable Oil
2 tsp. Vanilla

Combine dry ingredients in large mixer bowl. Add Eggs, Milk, Oil and Vanilla. Stir in boiling Water. Pour in greased pan. Bake at 350 degrees for 30 minutes in a 9" x 13" cake pan.

Disappearing Molasses Cookies

3 cups Shortening, melted
4 cups Sugar
5 Eggs
1 cup Molasses
2 tsp. Salt

1 tsp. Cinnamon
8 1/2 cups Flour
2 Tbsp + 2 tsp. Baking Soda

Melt shortening. Add sugar, Eggs, Molasses, Salt and Cinnamon. Add flour and Baking Soda. Form into balls, roll in sugar. Place on cookie sheet. Do not press down. Bake at 350 degrees.

Double Chocolate Crunch Bars

1/2 cup Oleo
2 beaten Eggs
3/4 cup Flour
1/4 tsp. Baking Powder
3/4 cup White Sugar
1 tsp. Vanilla
1 Tbsp. Cocoa
1/4 tsp. Salt

Spread in pan. Bake at 350 degrees oven for 15 to 20 minutes. Spread with 2 1/2 cups mini-marshmallows. Bake 2 to 3 minutes.

Dump Cake

1 can Cherry Pie Filling
1 can Crushed Pineapple, undrained
1 box dry Yellow Cake Mix
1/2 cup Butter, chopped
1 cup chopped Nuts, optional

Layer ingredients in a greased 9" x 12" loaf pan as listed. Bake at 350 degrees for 30-40 minutes. Delicious with ice cream. This is an easy cake for children, since you just dump everything in the pan!

Foster Willis Cookies

2 cups Brown Sugar
1 cup Shortening
2 Eggs
4 1/2 cups Flour (approximately)
2 tsp. Baking Soda
5 tsp. Baking Powder
1 tsp. Salt

1   tsp. Vanilla
1   cup Cream or Evaporated Milk
2 1/2   cups Miniature Chocolate chips
    Mix. Drop on lightly greased cookie sheets. Bake at 350 degrees until nicely browned.

Fresh Fruit Dessert Pizza

1   can Sweetened Condensed Milk
1/2   cup Sour Cream
1/4   cup Lemon Juice
1   tsp. Vanilla

Pizza Crust:

1/2   cup Margarine
1/4   cup Brown Sugar
1   cup Flour
1/4   cup Oats
1/4   cup Walnuts
Assorted fresh or canned fruit

    Combine first 4 ingredients in a bowl. Mix well. Chill. In a large bowl, beat next 5 ingredients until thoroughly blended. Press into 12" pizza round pan. Bake for 10-12 minutes, cool. Spread filling on crust. Arrange fruit on top of filling. Chill before serving.

Fresh Strawberry Pudding
Crust:

1 1/2   cups Flour
2   Tbsp. White Sugar
1/2   cup softened Butter

    Blend with Pastry Blender and press into 9" x 13" pan and bake at 425 degrees until lightly browned and then cool.

Filling:

2-3   boxes Strawberry Jell-O®
1/2   cups Clear Jel®
1 1/2   cups White Sugar
1/2   tsp. Salt
4   cups cold Water

    Cook until thickened, cool, add fresh Strawberries, pour filling over crust and top with Whipped Topping. Yummy

Fruit & Cream Pie

1   cup Sugar
1   cup Heavy Cream (do not beat)
3   Tbsp. Flour
1   Egg, beaten
Pinch of Salt
2   cups chopped Fruit-Can use, Apples, Peaches, Strawberries or Rhubarb.
       All of these have to be fresh. Mix well. Pour into unbaked Pie Shell. Bake at 400 degrees for about an hour.

Fudge Brownies

  1   cup Sugar
1/3   cup Cocoa
1/3   cup Melted Butter
1/2   tsp. Baking Powder
  1   tsp. Vanilla
  2   unbeaten Eggs
1/4   tsp. Salt
3/4   cup Flour
  1   cup Nuts
       Combine ingredients. Bake at 350 degrees for 25 minutes. When cool, cut in squares.

Good Chocolate Frosting

1/2   cup Butter
  6   Tbsp. Milk
1/4   cup Cocoa
  1   lb. Powdered Sugar
       Bring to a boil and add Powdered Sugar; stir well. Cool completely; spread over cake.

Granola Bars

1/2   lb. Butter or Oleo
1/4   cup Vegetable Oil
1/4   cup Honey

1/4   cup Peanut Butter

2   pkgs. Mini Marshmallows

     Over low heat melt above ingredients, stir constantly

5   cups Oatmeal

4 1/2   cups Rice Krispies®

2   pks. Graham Crackers

2   cups Coconut

1   cup or more miniature M & M's®

1   cup Chocolate Chips

1   cup crushed Peanuts or Almonds (optional)

     Mix above ingredients in a large bowl, then pour top mixture over dry ingredients and stir. Add Chocolate Chips last. Press in Texas Sheet Cake Pans & cool, and cut desired size.

Hot Caramel Dumplings
Dough:

1 1/4   cups Flour

1/2   cup Sugar

1 1/2   tsp. Baking Powder

1/8   tsp. Salt

1   tsp. Butter

1/2   tsp. Vanilla

1   cup Milk

Sauce:

1   tsp. Butter

1 1/2   cups Boiling Water

1   cup Brown Sugar

1/8   tsp. Salt

     Put in kettle & let come to boil while preparing dough. Sift dry ingredients together, cut in Butter. Add Milk, Vanilla & mix. Drop by spoonfuls in boiling sauce. Boil lightly over low heat 10 minutes without removing cover.

Ice Cream Sandwich

2   cups Graham Crackers (crushed)

1/2   cup melted Butter

1/4   cup Brown Sugar

     Press in a cake pan; but leave 1/2 for the top.

Pudding

1 1/2   cup Milk
  3/4   cup Brown Sugar
  1/4   cup Flour
    6   Egg Yolks
Salt & Flavoring

    Cook pudding ingredients together for a few minutes and allow to cool. Beat 6 Egg Whites and 2 cups Cream and add this to the pudding. Put pudding on cracker crumbs and the rest of crumbs on top. Freeze.

Jiffy Chocolate Feather Cake

  3   cups Flour
  2   cups Sugar
  2   tsp. Baking Soda
  2   tsp. Baking Powder
  1   tsp. Salt
1/2   cup Unsweetened Cocoa
  1   cup Vegetable Oil
  1   cup Milk
  1   cup Prepared Coffee
  2   Eggs
  1   tsp. Vanilla

    Mix dry ingredients together first. Add Vegetable oil, milk and coffee. Stir well. Add Eggs and Vanilla and beat until smooth. Pour in a 9" x 13" pan. Bake at 350 degrees until done.

Jimmy Carter Pudding
First layer:

  1   cup Flour
2/3   cup chopped Salted Peanuts
  1   stick Oleo

    Mix and press in 9" x 13" inch pan. Bake at 350 degrees for 20 minutes, cool.

Second Layer:

1/3   cup Peanut Butter
  8   oz. Cream Cheese
  1   cup Powdered Sugar

1   cup Whip Cream

Third Layer:
1 3   oz. box Instant Chocolate Pudding
2 3/4   cups Milk
1 3   oz. box Instant Vanilla Pudding

Fourth Layer:
Whip Cream to cover, sprinkle with Chopped Peanuts

M & M® Bars

2   cups Oatmeal
1   cup Brown Sugar
1 1/2   cups Flour
1   tsp. Baking Soda
Salt and Vanilla each to taste
1   cup Mini M & M's®
1   cup Butter, melted
1/3   cup Peanut Butter
1   can Sweetened Condensed Milk

Combine Oats, Flour, Sugar, Soda and Salt. Add Butter. Mix until dry ingredients are moist. Reserve 1 cup crumbs. Press remaining crumbs into bottom of 9" x 13" inch pan. Bake at 350 degrees for 12 minutes. Combine Condensed Milk and Peanut Butter in small bowl. Spread over partially baked crust. Combine reserved crumbs and M & M's®. Sprinkle over top, pressing down lightly. Bake 20 minutes longer! Delicious & Tasty if not over baked!

Moist Marble Cake
Dark Part:

3   cups Flour
2   cups Sugar
4   Tbsp. Cocoa
2   tsp. Baking Soda
1/2   tsp. Salt
3/4   cup Corn Oil
2   Tbsp. Vinegar
1   Tbsp. Vanilla
2   cups Cold Water

For Dark Part; sift together dry ingredients. Add remaining ingredients. Mix well; set aside.

Light Part:

3/4	cup Shortening
1 1/2	cups Sugar
2	tsp. Vanilla
2	Eggs
3	cups Flour
3	tsp. Baking Powder
1/2	tsp. Salt
1	cup Milk

For Light Part; In another bowl, cream together Shortening, Sugar, Vanilla and Eggs. Sift dry ingredients, add to cream mixture alternately with milk. Mix well. Swirl batters in a 10 x 15 pan. Bake at 375 degrees. Frost when cool; freezing gives the cake extra moistness.

Monster Cookies

12	Eggs
1	lb. Butter or Margarine
3	lbs. or 6 cups Peanut Butter
4	cups Brown Sugar
4	cups White Sugar
2	Tbsp. Vanilla
1	Tbsp. clear Karo®
8	tsp. Baking Soda
18	cups Oatmeal
1	lb. Chocolate Chips
1	lb. Baking M & M's®
2	cups nut or more if desired
1	lb raisins

Mix in order given. Drop on greased cookie sheets. Bake at 350 degrees about 12 minutes. Do not over bake.

No Egg Chocolate Cake

2 1/2	cup Flour
1/2	cup Cocoa
1/8	tsp. Salt

2   cups Brown Sugar
1/2   cup Buttermilk or Sour Milk
1   tsp. Vanilla
1/2   cup hot Water
1   tsp. Baking Soda

Sift together Flour, Cocoa and Salt. Add Brown Sugar, Buttermilk and Vanilla. Beat well, then add Water and Soda. Beat again. Bake at 350 degrees for about 40 minutes.

Old Fashioned Ice Cream

4   qt. Milk
3   cups Brown Sugar
8   Tbsp. Flour

Heat all of the above ingredients. Beat in 16 eggs and simmer 10 minutes. Add 6 Tbsp. Vanilla. Add 3 cups of Cream. Use electric or hand crank Ice Cream Freezer. This is for 1 1/2 gal. freezer. I also put a little salt and Maple Flavor in.

Peach Cream Pie

3   cups sliced Peaches
1   cup Cream, unbeaten
1   cup Sugar
1/4   cup Flour
1   unbaked Pie Shell

Mix together Peaches and Cream. Add Flour to Sugar; mix with Peaches. Pour into Pie Shell. Bake at 400 degrees until done.

Peach Crisp

6   cups fresh Peaches
1/3   cup Whole Wheat or Rye Flour
1   cup Oatmeal
1/3   cup Butter, melted

Preheat oven to 375 degrees. Place Peaches in baking dish. Combine dry ingredients, add Butter and mix till crumbly. Sprinkle on top of Peaches. Bake 30 minutes.

Pecan Pie

3 Eggs slightly beaten
1/2 cup Brown Sugar
1 cup Light Corn Syrup-with a little water added
1 Tbsp. Flour
1 Tbsp. Butter melted
1/2 tsp. Salt
1 cup Pecans or Walnuts
1 tsp. Vanilla

Mix all together and add one cup Pecans or Walnuts last. Pour into unbaked pie crust and bake at 350 degrees as you would for custard pie. Bake about 35-45 minutes.

Kentucky Pecan Pie

1 cup White Corn Syrup
1/2 cup Brown Sugar
1/4 cup melted Butter or Oleo
1 tsp. Vanilla
1/3 tsp. Salt
4 Eggs, slightly beaten
1 cup Pecans
1 cup Rice Krispies® (if you wish)

Combine Syrup, Sugar, Salt, Butter and Vanilla and mix well. Add Eggs and Pecans last. Bake in oven 350 degrees for about 45 minutes or until done!

Pumpkin Bars

4 Eggs
1 2/3 cups Sugar
1 cup Salad Oil
1-16 oz. can Pumpkin
2 cups Flour
2 tsp. Baking Powder
2 tsp. Cinnamon
1 tsp. Salt
1 tsp. Baking Soda

In mixing bowl beat together Eggs, Sugar, Oil & Pumpkin until fluffy. Stir together Flour, Baking Powder, Cinnamon, Salt & Soda. Add to Pumpkin mixture & mix. Bake in 350 degree oven for 25-30 minutes. Cool & frost with Cream Cheese Frosting.

Frosting:

1-3 oz. Cream Cheese softened
1/2 cup Butter or Margarine
1 tsp. Vanilla
2 cups Powder Sugar

Cream together Cheese and Margarine, stir in Vanilla, add Powder Sugar.

Pumpkin Sheet Cake

16 oz. can Pumpkin
2 cups Sugar
3/4 cup Vegetable Oil
4 Eggs, lightly beaten
2 cups Flour
2 tsp. Baking Soda
1 tsp. Cinnamon
1/2 tsp. Salt

Put in greased pan (15" x 10" x 1"). Bake at 350 degrees for 25-30 minutes.

Frosting:

3 oz. Cream Cheese
5 tsp. Butter
1 tsp. Vanilla
3-4 tsp. Milk

Mix together, spread on cake. Top with chopped Nuts if desired.

Quick Caramel Icing

6 Tbsp. Milk
6 Tbsp. butter
3/4 cup Brown Sugar
2 cups Powdered Sugar

Mix sugar and butter and blend. Add milk and bring to a boil. Remove from heat and gradually add Powdered Sugar.

Ranger Joe Cookies

1   cup Shortening
1   cup Sugar
1   cup Brown Sugar
2   Eggs
1   tsp. Vanilla
1/2   cup Chocolate Chips
2   cups Rice Krispies®
2   cups Quick Oats
1   tsp. Baking Soda
1   tsp. Baking Powder
2   cups Flour
1/2   cup Nuts, chopped
1/2   tsp. Salt

Beat the first 5 ingredients. Add the rest. Roll into balls and place on cookie sheets. Flatten with fork. Bake 350 degrees 12 to 15 minutes.

Reese's® Cake Squares

1   cup Butter
4   Tbsp. Cocoa
1   cup Water
2   cups Flour
2   cups Sugar
1   tsp. Baking Powder
2   Eggs
1   tsp. Vanilla
Peanut Butter

Bring Butter, Cocoa and Water to a boil. Pour over dry ingredients. Add Eggs and Vanilla. Pour into greased 10" x 15" baking sheet. Bake at 350 degrees for 20 minutes. When cooled, spread a layer of Peanut Butter on top.

Frosting:

1/2   cup Butter
4   Tbsp. Cocoa
6   Tbsp. Buttermilk
1   Tbsp. Vanilla
Powdered Sugar

Heat everything but Powdered Sugar. Add Powdered Sugar and spread evenly over Peanut Butter. You may substitute 5 Tbsp. Milk & 1 Tbsp. Vinegar for Buttermilk.

Rhubarb Pie

2 cups diced Rhubarb
2 Tbsp. Flour (scant)
1 cup White Sugar
1 tsp. Vanilla

Crumbs:

3/4 cup Flour
1/3 cup Butter
1/2 cup Brown Sugar

Mix first 4 ingredients together & put in unbaked pie shell. Mix last 3 ingredients till crumbly & put on top of filling. Bake at 400 degrees for 10 minutes then reduce to 350 degrees for 30 minutes.

Rhubarb Cream Pie

2 cups Rhubarb
2/3 cup Brown Sugar
2 Eggs
2 Tbsp. Flour
1/2 cup Cream

Mix Sugar and Flour together. Add Egg Yolks and Cream, mix well. Add cut Rhubarb; pour in an unbaked pie shell. Bake in 425 degrees oven till Rhubarb is tender and filling set. Beat Egg Whites, add 3 Tbsp. Brown Sugar, 1 Tbsp. Real Lemon®. Pour over baked pie and bake till golden brown.

Rich Chocolate Cake

2 cups Brown Sugar
1 tsp. Salt
2 tsp. Baking Powder
2/3 cup melted Shortening
2 cups boiling Water
2 tsp. Vanilla
3/4 cup Cocoa
2 tsp. Baking Soda
2 1/4 cups Flour

2   Eggs
Nuts, optional

Mix together all dry ingredients. Add Shortening, Water, Vanilla and Eggs. Beat together for 2 minutes. Add Nuts. Bake at 350 degrees until done 35 - 40 minutes.

Shortcake

2   cups Flour
3   tsp. Baking Powder
1/8   tsp. Salt
1/3   cup Sugar
1/3   cup Shortening
2/3   cup Milk

Mix together Flour, Baking Powder, Salt and Sugar. Cut in Shortening, add Milk, mix lightly bake at 350 degrees for about 25 minutes. Serve with Milk or Cream. Add your favorite fresh sweetened berries or fruit.

Twix® Bars

Graham Crackers
1/2   cup White Sugar
1/3   cup Milk
1   cup Graham Cracker Crumbs
1   stick Butter
3/4   cup Brown Sugar
1   cup Chocolate Chips
3/4   cup Peanut Butter

Line a 9" x 13" cake pan with whole Graham Crackers. Boil together the Butter, Sugars, Graham Cracker Crumbs and Milk. Cook for 5 minutes. Pour over the Graham Crackers. Add another layer of Graham Crackers. Melt the Chocolate Chips & Peanut Butter, spread on top of Graham Crackers, cool.

MAIN DISHES

The same fire that melts butter hardens the egg.

Country Chicken and Biscuits

3	Carrots
1/2	cup Onions
2 1/2	cups diced Chicken
3	cups cubed Potatoes
1	bag Peas
1 1/2	cups Grated Cheese
1-2	cans Cream of Chicken soup

Biscuit Dough

Slice Carrots and chop Onions, cook veggies and Potatoes. Mix all ingredients except Biscuits together and add Milk to desired thickness. Bake at 325 degrees for 2 hours. Top with Biscuit Dough and bake until golden brown.

Delicious Meat Loaf

2	lbs. Ground Beef
2	cups Cornflakes
1	Egg
1	small Onion chopped

Salt & Pepper to taste

1	can Tomato Soup

Form into loaf and bake at 350 degrees for 1 hour, uncovered.

Long John Silvers® Fish Batter

1 Egg White
1 tsp. Salt
3 tsp. Baking Powder
1 cup Flour
1 tsp. Oil
3/4 cup Water
3 1/2 lbs. Fish

Beat Egg Whites until stiff. Mix Baking Powder, Oil, Salt and Water; add to Egg Whites. Dip Fish into mixture and deep fat fry. Can be used for any deep fat frying.

Yummy Settic

1 lb. Hamburger
1 can Mushroom Soup
1 can Tomato Sauce
1 lb. Cheese
1 pkg. Noodles
Salt to taste

Fry Hamburger, cook the Noodles in hot water. Mix Tomato Sauce with Hamburger and Mushroom Soup, with Noodles, cover with Cheese. Bake at 325 for 1 hour.

MISCELLANEOUS

Kindness is a hard thing to get rid of - it usually comes back.

Bar-B-Q-Sauce

1/2 lb. Butter or Oleo (1 cup)
1 pt. Water
1 pt. Vinegar
4 Tbsp. Salt
2 Tbsp. Worcestershire® Sauce
1/2 tsp. Tabasco® Sauce

Bring to a boil. Brush on chicken as you like.

Best Caramel Corn

7 qt. unsalted warm pop-corn
2 cups Brown Sugar
1/2 cup Light Karo® or Corn Syrup
1 cup Butter
1/2 tsp. Baking Soda

Mix Sugar, Corn Syrup and Butter. Cook for 5 minutes, remove from heat, add Soda; stir. Immediately pour over pop-corn; mix well. Set the whole bowl in oven at 250 degrees and bake for 1 hour, stirring every 10-15 minutes.

Butterscotch Sauce

1 1/2 cups Brown Sugar
1/3 cup Corn Syrup
4 Tbsp. Butter
1/2 tsp. Vanilla
1/2 cup Cream

Cook Sugar, Corn Syrup and Butter to a Soft Ball. Stir to keep from scorching. Remove from heat and add Vanilla and Cream. Beat until smooth. Good on ice-cream.

Cheese Ball

2   (3 oz.) Dried Beef
2   (8 oz.) Cream Cheese
1 1/2   tsp. Garlic Powder
1 1/2   tsp. Parsley Flakes
1 1/2   tsp. Onion Salt
1 1/2   tsp. Accent®

Finely cut Dried Beef and mix with Cream Cheese. Add spices and mix well. Form in a ball and chill.

Chocolate Chip Cheese Ball

8   oz. Cream Cheese (softened)
1/2   cup Butter (softened)
1/2   tsp. Vanilla
3/4   cup Powdered Sugar
3/4   cup Mini Chocolate Chips
2   tsp. Brown Sugar

Beat Cream Cheese, butter and vanilla until fluffy. Add sugars. Beat until just combined. Stir in Chocolate Chips; cover and refrigerate for 2 hours. Serve with Graham Crackers. Enjoy!

Creamy Caramel Dip

1   pkg. 8 oz. Cream Cheese (softened)
1   cup Sour cream
2   tsp. Vanilla
1   cup cold Milk
1   box Instant Vanilla Pudding
Fresh Fruit

In a bowl, beat Cream Cheese and Brown Sugar until smooth. Add Sour Cream, Vanilla, milk and pudding. Beat well. Cover and refrigerate for at least 1 hour. Serve as a dip for fruit.

Creamy Horseradish Dip

1-18 oz. Cream Cheese
1/2   cup Mayonnaise
1/3   cup Horseradish
1/4   cup green Onion, chopped
4   Tbsp. Bacon, chopped

Combine Cheese, Mayonnaise and Horseradish until well blended. Stir in green Onion and Bacon. Serve with Vegetables or Chips.

Fruit Dip

2   cups Pineapple Juice
2   Tbsp. Clear Jel®
1/2   cup Sugar
9   oz. Cool Whip
8   oz. Cream Cheese

Cook Juice, Sugar and Clear Jel® until thick. When cool, add Cool Whip and Cream Cheese. Mix together until creamy. Serve with your favorite fresh fruits.

Gooey Snackin' Pizza
Crust:

1/2   cup Sugar
1/2   cup Brown Sugar, packed
1/2   cup Butter, softened
1/2   cup Peanut Butter
1/2   tsp. Vanilla
1   Egg
1 1/2 cups Flour
1/2   cup Miniature Semi Sweet Chocolate Chips
7   oz. jar Marshmallow Cream

Heat oven to 375 degrees. In large bowl combine Sugar, Butter, Peanut Butter, Vanilla and Egg; blend well. Lightly spoon Flour into measuring cup; mix well. Press dough evenly over bottom & half way up edges of ungreased 12 or 14 inch Pizza Pan. Bake at 375 degrees for 15 to 20 minutes or until center is set. Drop Marshmallow Cream by tablespoon onto crust. Let stand for 2 minutes to soften, spread with wet knife. Sprinkle with topping choices. Bake at 375 degrees for 2-3 minutes. Drizzle sauce over finished pizza. Cut into wedges.

Sauce:

24 Caramels
 2 Tbsp. Milk

     Sauce: In medium saucepan over low heat, melt caramels; stir constantly. Toppings: Nuts, Coconut, Maraschino Cherries, Chocolate Chips, Rice Krispies®, Chopped Candy bars and/or Fudge Ice Cream.

Illegal Dip

2 lbs. Hamburger
1 lb. Velveeta®
1 can Refried Beans
1 pt. Salsa

     Fry Hamburger and drain. Add rest of ingredients. Cook until heated through.

Krebbles

    1 qt. Liver Pudding
3/4 cup White Flour
3/4 cup Cornmeal
1 1/2 qt. Water
Salt and Pepper to taste.

     Cook until thick, about 10 minutes. pour into loaf pan. Slice and fry in Butter. Very Good!

Mock Zucchini Dressing

    2 cups coarsely grated Zucchini
1 1/2 cups Cracker Crumbs
    1 stick Margarine
1/3 cup chopped Onions
    3 Eggs, beaten
1/2 cup shredded Cheese

     Melt Margarine in large saucepan. Let cool 5 minutes. Stir in Zucchini, Onions, Eggs, Cheese and Crackers. Butter 2 qt. baking dish and bake uncovered at 350 degrees for 50 minutes.

Party Mix

1   large box Cheerios®
1   box Rice Chex® Cereal
1   box Corn Chex® Cereal
1   bag Pretzel Sticks broken up
2   boxes Kix® Cereal
1   lb. Peanuts or Cashews
3   tsp. Savory Salt
3   tsp. Celery Salt
3   tsp. Garlic Salt
4   tsp. Worcestershire® Sauce
1/2   lb Butter

Combine the salts, sauce, butter and heat. Mix together the cereals, nuts and pretzels and pour salty mixture over top. Place in large cookie sheets and heat in 300 degrees oven for 15 minutes, stirring mixture occasionally for even coating.

Peach Slush

4   cups Sugar
4   cups Water
1   pkg. sliced Peaches
8   Bananas
2-20   oz. cans diced Pineapples
1-8   oz. can Frozen Orange Juice

Cook Sugar and Water together. Add to fruit mixture. Put in plastic freezer boxes and freeze.

Rhubarb Preserves

5   cups Rhubarb, chopped
4   cups Sugar
1   cup crushed Pineapple
1/2   cup Jell-O®

Mix and cook Rhubarb, Sugar and Pineapple for 15 minutes. Take from heat and add Jell-O® (can use Strawberry or Orange). Stir well and put in jars and seal.

Salsa

    5   gal. Tomatoes
    4   qt. chopped Onions
    4   qt. chopped Peppers
    2   cups chopped Garlic
1 1/2   qt. Vinegar
  1/8   cup Salt

Peel and squeeze out seeds from Tomatoes, then crush & simmer till rest of ingredients simmer another 1/2 hour. Put in jars, cold pack 10 minutes.

Salty Garlic Dill Pickles

    2   qt. Water
1 1/2   cups Vinegar
  1/2   cup Salt (scant)

Slice cucumbers thin and pack in jars, add a clove of Garlic or 1/8 tsp. Garlic Powder and a head of Dill. Pour Vinegar Water to 3/4 full. Cold pack in just to the boiling point. Turn off heat and let set in hot water till cool.

Sausage Cheese Mix

    1   lb. Sausage
    1   can Cheddar Cheese Soup
  1/2   cup Milk
    3   cups Biscuit Baking Mix

* Cook Sausage in skillet, drain, add soup and Milk. Stir in Biscuit Mix just until moistened. Fill greased muffin cups 2/3 full. Bake at 400 degrees for 15 to 20 minutes or until done.

School Boys Delight Pickles

   12   med. size cucumbers
    4   med. size Green Peppers
    6   cups Vinegar
    2   cups Water
1 1/2   tsp. Turmeric
    8   med. size Onions
    7   cups Sugar
    4   tsp. Mustard Seed
    2   tsp. Celery Seed

Slice Pickles, Onion and Peppers. Stir together Sugar, Vinegar, Water, Mustard Seed, Turmeric and Celery Seed until dissolved. Let stand.. Pour over Pickles, Onions and Green Peppers. Store in refrigerator or cold pack. Ready to eat in 24 hours. Can be put in jars and cold pack 5 minutes

Sweet Pepper Butter

42	sweet Peppers
1	pt. Yellow Mustard
1	qt. Vinegar
6	cups Sugar
1	Tbsp. Salt
1	cup Flour
1 1/2	cups Water

Grind Peppers, add Mustard, Sugar and Salt, bring to a boil. Add to boiling mixture and cook 5 minutes (flour paste). Pour in jars and seal. Makes 8 pints.

Sweet N Sour Dressing

1	cup Sugar
1	cup Oil

Beat these two together, then it won't separate.
Add 1 Tbsp. Salad Dressing

2	Tbsp. Mustard
1	small Onion (grated)
1/4	cup Vinegar
1	tsp. Salt
1	tsp. Celery Seed
1/4	tsp. Black Pepper

Mix in order given & beat. Refrigerate.

Sugar Spread for Church

2	cups Brown Sugar
1	cup Sugar
1	cup dark Karo®
2	cups light Karo®

Boil 2 minutes. Let cool and add 3 Egg Whites, beaten well. Stir until cool. Can add vanilla or maple flavoring.

Yum Yums Candy

2   cups Peanut Butter
2   cups Powder Sugar
3   cups Rice Krispies®
1/4 cup Butter

Combine and mix all ingredients together and roll into balls. Dip in Chocolate. Do not melt butter on stove.

SALADS

Trouble shared is trouble halved.
Joy shared is joy doubled.

Christmas Salad

1   lg. pkg. Lime Jell-O®
1   lg. pkg. Red Jell-O®
1   can Crushed Pineapple
2   cups Marshmallows
1   pkg. Cream Cheese
1/2   cup Nuts (chopped)

Dissolve Lime Jell-O® in 2 cups boiling water; add marshmallows while hot, add cream cheese and beat with mixer until cheese is whipped in. Add 2 cups cold water, cool; add nuts and pineapple. Chill but before completely firm, add a layer of red Jell-O®. Dissolve the same as green layer, only leave plain. Top off with a spoon of whipped cream and cherry.

Crunchy "Leanna" Coleslaw

4   cups Cabbage, coarsely chopped
1   cup Grapes
1   small Red Apple, optional
1   cup Walnuts, toasted
1   Tbsp. Butter
2   Tbsp. Brown Sugar

Dressing:

3/4   cup Mayonnaise
1/3   cup Lemon Pie Filling

63

1 tsp. Vinegar
1/4 tsp. Celery Seed
1/8 tsp. Salt

Five Cup Salad

1 cup Sour Cream
1 cup Mandarin Oranges, drained
1 cup Marshmallows
1 cup Coconut
1 cup crushed Pineapple, drained
   In a large bowl, mix all ingredients; chill. Yield: 8 servings.

Frozen Fruit Salad

1-8 oz. Cream Cheese
1 1/2 cups White Sugar
3 cups Whipped Topping
1 Qt. Strawberries mashed
8 Bananas mashed
1 can Crushed Pineapple
   Mix Cream Cheese and Sugar, add rest of ingredients and freeze. Enjoy!

Lime Salad

2 cups Pastry Flour
1/2 cup melted Butter
1/2 cup Brown Sugar
1/2 cup chopped Nuts
   Mix and press into a 9" x 13" cake pan. Bake at 350 degrees for 20 to 25 minutes. Meanwhile drain 1 can Crushed Pineapples. Place juice in a saucepan and bring to a boil. Dissolve 6 oz. Lime Jell-O® in Pineapple Juice. Cool. Cream 1 (8 oz.) Cream Cheese with 1 cup White Sugar. Blend in Jell-O® also add the Pineapples which were drained. Chill 1 can Evaporated Milk then whip the milk until nice and fluffy. Mix into Jell-O® mixture. Pour Jell-O® mixture on top of crust, then let set. Dissolve 2 boxes Jell-O® in 4 cups boiling water. When Jell-O® starts to set, pour on top of Jell-O® mixture. Yummy!

Orange Crust Salad

2 cups Flour
1/2 cup Brown Sugar
1/2 cup Nuts
1 cup Oleo
1 can crushed Pineapples
1 3 oz. pkg. Orange Jell-O®
1 8 oz. pkg. Cream Cheese
1 cup White Sugar
1 cup chilled Evaporated Milk

Mix Flour, Brown Sugar, Nuts and Oleo and press into cake pan and bake at 350 degrees for 15 minutes. Don't let it get too brown or crust will get hard. Drain crushed Pineapples into sauce pan. Bring juice to a boil, dissolve Jell-O® in Juice, cool. Cream Cheese with White Sugar. Blend into Jell-O® and stir in the Pineapples. Whip chilled Evaporated Milk. Then mix everything together and pat on top of crust. Keep chilled.

Potato Salad

12 cups Potatoes, cook and put through Salad Master® when cooked
12 hard cooked Eggs-Mash with Potato Masher
1/2 cup medium Onion
2 cups chopped Celery

Dressing Combine:

3 cups Mayonnaise
6 Tbsp. Yellow Prepared Mustard
2 tsp. Salt
2 1/2 cups White Sugar
1/4 cup Vinegar
1/2 cup Milk

Also put in shredded Carrots if preferred.

Serves 1 gallon. Best if made 1 day ahead.

SIDE DISHES

A merry heart does good like a medicine,
but a broken spirit dries the bones.

Marinated Carrots

2   lb. cooked Carrots
1   sliced Onion
1   chopped Green Pepper
3/4 cup Vinegar
1/2 tsp. mustard
1   can Tomato Soup
1   tsp. Worcestershire® Sauce
3/4 cup White Sugar
1/2 cup Salad Oil

Mix last six ingredients, heat and pour over carrots and onions. Place in refrigerator overnight.

Macaroni and Cheese

4   cups Elbow Macaroni
6   cups Milk
2   tsp. Worcestershire® Sauce
2   lb. Cheddar Cheese (substitute other types of cheese as desired)
Sprinkle Paprika
1   tsp. Salt

Mix ingredients in casserole dish. Cover with aluminum foil. Bake at 350 45 to 50 minutes.

Mixed Bean Burger Casserole

1   1/2 lbs. ground Beef
1   small Onion
1/2 tsp. Salt
1   can Kidney Beans
1   can Lima Beans
1   can Pork and Beans
1/2 cup Ketchup
2   Tbsp. Vinegar
3   Tbsp. Brown Sugar
1/2 tsp. Dry Mustard

Brown meat in skillet; mix with other ingredients. Bake at 350 degrees for 30 minutes.

Potluck Potatoes

2   lb. Potatoes
2   Tbsp. Butter
1   tsp. Salt
1   tsp. Pepper
1   medium Onion, chopped
1   can Cream of Mushroom Soup
1   pt. Sour Cream
2   cups Velveeta® Cheese
2   cups Corn Flakes, crumbs
1/4 cup Butter, melted

Cook Potatoes until almost tender. Dice, add melted Butter, Salt, Pepper, Onion, soup, Sour Cream and cheese. Blend thoroughly and pour into casserole dish. Cover with Corn Flake crumbs mixed with 1/4 cup Butter. Bake at 350 degrees for 45 minutes. Serves 8 people. Delicious dinner!

Zucchini Patties

2/3 cup Bisquick® Mix
1/4 cup Parmesan Cheese
2   Eggs beaten
2   cups grated Zucchini
1   small Onion, chopped
Salt and Pepper

Combine the ingredients and drop by spoonfuls into heavy skillet containing a thin layer of Margarine. Spread out and flatten as you turn them with a spatula. Fry until golden brown on both sides.

TIPS IN THE KITCHEN

"This is the day the Lord has made
let us rejoice and be glad in it"

* Dip a tomato in boiling water for 1/2 to 1 minute, then into cold water and the skin will slip off easily.

* Put a piece of bread with cookies to keep them soft.

* Add 1/2 cup Sour Cream to your Peanut Butter Cookie recipes to make your cookies more moist.

* To keep boiled syrup from crystallizing add a pinch of Baking Soda.

* Put some Vinegar in your Bread-Dough to help it stay fresher longer.

* To crisp up Celery or Lettuce, place it in a pan of cold Water with a peeled, raw Potato.

* If you shake an Egg and it rattles, you can be sure it's stale. A really fresh Egg will sink and a stale one will float if you place it in Water.

* Adding a pinch of Salt to Jell-O®, improves flavor.

* To cut a fresh cake, use a thin sharp knife dipped in water.

* Adding salt to oil before frying helps control splatter.

27219390R00040

Made in the USA
Lexington, KY
01 November 2013